3 *After* each note write a *higher* note to form the named *melodic* interval, as show
first answer. The key is G major.

5th   4th   7th

3rd   8th/8ve   2nd

4 (a) Name the degree of the scale (e.g. 2nd, 3rd, 4th) of each of the notes marked *,   [10]
as shown in the first answer. The key is C major.

Mozart

5th
....

(b) Draw a circle around the *lowest* note in the melody.

5 Write the time values ♩ 𝅝 ♪ 𝅗𝅥 ♪ 𝅗𝅥.   [10]
in the correct order, from the *shortest* to the *longest*. The first answer is given.

♪
....

3

6 Next to each note write a rest that has the same time value, as shown in the first answer. [10]

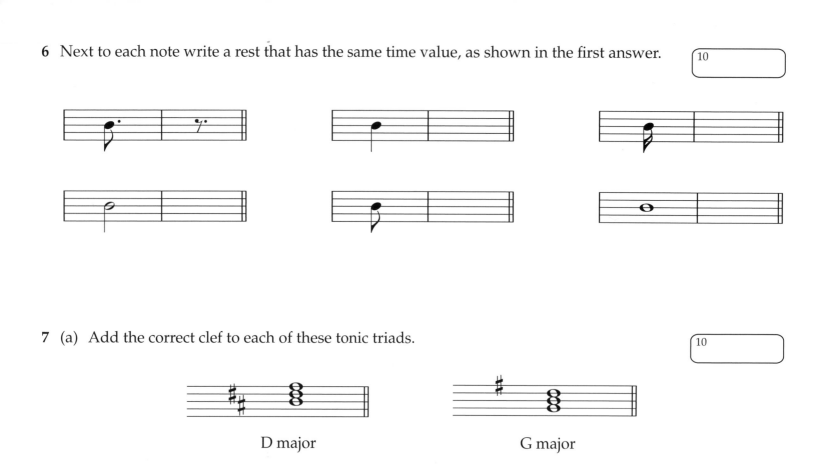

7 (a) Add the correct clef to each of these tonic triads. [10]

D major   G major

Letter names   ……… ……… ………   ……… ……… ………

(b) Under each triad write the letter name of each note, including the sharp sign where necessary.

Music Theory Past Papers 2016

ABRSM Grade 1

Theory Paper   Grade 1   2016 · A

Duration 1½ hours

Candidates should answer ALL questions.
Write your answers on this paper – no others will be accepted.
Answers must be written clearly and neatly – otherwise marks may be lost.

TOTAL MARKS
100

1 (a) Add the time signature to each of these three melodies.

10

(b) Add the missing bar-lines to this melody. The first bar-line is given.

2 Write a two-bar rhythm as an answer to the given rhythm.

10

8 Look at this melody, which is adapted from a piece by Verdi, and then answer the questions below.

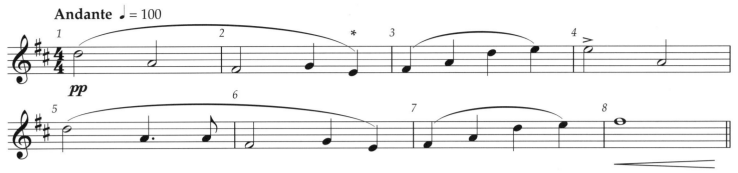

Write your answer to question (c) on the stave below.

(a) Give the meaning of:

    Andante ....

    ♩ = 100 ....

    pp ....

    > (bar 4) ....

    ⟍ (bar 8) ....

(b) (i) Give the time name (e.g. crotchet or
        quarter note) of the *longest* note in the melody. ....

   (ii) Complete this sentence:
        Bars 2 and 3 have the same notes and rhythm as bars .... and ....

   (iii) Underline one of the following words that best describes how you think bars 5–6
        should be played.

                legato (smoothly)   or   *staccato* (detached)

   (iv) This melody is in the key of D major. Give the number of
        a bar that contains all the notes of the tonic triad in this key.   Bar ....

   (v) Give the letter name of the last note in bar 2 (marked ∗). ....

(c) Copy out the music from the start of bar 1 to the end of bar 4, exactly as it is written
    above. Don't forget the clef, key signature, time signature, tempo marking, dynamic
    and all other details. Write the music on the blank stave above question (a). (Marks
    will be given for neatness and accuracy.)

Theory Paper   Grade 1   2016   B

Duration 1½ hours

Candidates should answer ALL questions.
Write your answers on this paper – no others will be accepted.
Answers must be written clearly and neatly – otherwise marks may be lost.

TOTAL MARKS
100

1 (a) Add the time signature to each of these three melodies.

10

Saint-Saëns

F. D. Philidor

Grieg

(b) Add the missing bar-lines to this melody. The first bar-line is given.

Reinecke

2 Write a two-bar rhythm as an answer to the given rhythm.

10

3 Add the correct clef and any necessary sharp or flat signs to make each of the scales named below. Do *not* use key signatures.

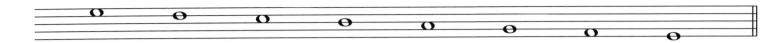

G major

F major

4 (a) Give the letter name of each of the notes marked ∗, including the sharp sign where necessary. The first answer is given.

G
....

(b) Draw a circle around two notes next to each other that are tied together.

5 Add a rest at the places marked ∗ in these two melodies to make each bar complete.

6 Rewrite the following melody, grouping (beaming) the notes correctly.

Arne

7 Add the correct clef to make each of these named notes, as shown in the first answer.

C   Bb   D

B   middle C   F   A

E   G   C#   F#

8 Look at this melody by Robert Lindley and then answer the questions below.

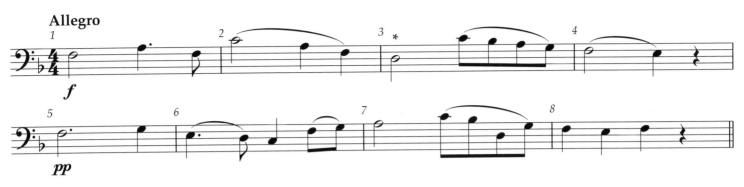

Write your answer to question (c) on the stave below.

(a) Give the meaning of:

Allegro ....

the lower **4** in **4/4** ....

f ....

pp (bar 5) ....

⌢ (e.g. bar 3) ....

10

(b) (i) Give the time name (e.g. crotchet or quarter note) of the *longest* note in the melody. ....

(ii) Give the letter name of the *highest* note in the melody. ....

(iii) How many bars contain a crotchet (quarter-note) rest? ....

(iv) This melody is in the key of F major. Draw a bracket (⌐▔▔¬) over three notes next to each other that form the tonic triad in this key.

(v) Name the degree of the scale (e.g. 2nd, 3rd, 4th) of the first note in bar 3 (marked ∗). Remember that the key is F major. ....

10

(c) Copy out the music from the start of bar 1 to the end of bar 4, exactly as it is written above. Don't forget the clef, key signature, time signature, tempo marking, dynamic and all other details. Write the music on the blank stave above question (a). (Marks will be given for neatness and accuracy.)

10

Theory Paper   Grade 1   2016   C

Duration 1½ hours

Candidates should answer ALL questions.
Write your answers on this paper – no others will be accepted.
Answers must be written clearly and neatly – otherwise marks may be lost.

TOTAL MARKS
100

1 Add the missing bar-lines to these two melodies. The first bar-line is given in each.

2 Write a two-bar rhythm as an answer to the given rhythm.

3 Write the tonic triads named below, using the correct key signature for each.

D major   F major

4 Add a rest at the places marked ∗ in these two melodies to make each bar complete.

5 Add the correct clef and any necessary sharp or flat signs to make each of the scales named below. Do *not* use key signatures.

G major

D major

6 Give the number (e.g. 2nd, 3rd, 4th) of each of these harmonic intervals, as shown in the first answer. The key is C major.

6th
....

....

....

....

....

....

7 (a) Name the degree of the scale (e.g. 2nd, 3rd, 4th) of each of the notes marked ∗, as shown in the first answer. The key is F major.

Haydn

5th
....

(b) How many quavers (eighth notes) is the note in the last bar worth?   ....

8 Look at this melody, which is adapted from a piece by Weber, and then answer the questions below.

Write your answer to question (c) on the stave below.

(a) Give the meaning of: [10]

   Allegro ………………………………………………………………………………………

   the **2** in **2/4** ………………………………………………………………………………………

   ff ………………………………………………………………………………………

   the dots above the notes (e.g. bar 3) ……………………………………………………………

   ⌒ (e.g. bar 4) ………………………………………………………………………………

(b) (i)   Give the time name (e.g. crotchet or [10]
        quarter note) of the *shortest rest* in the melody. ……………………………………

  (ii) Complete this sentence:
      Bar 2 has the same notes and rhythm as bar ……… .

  (iii) Draw a circle around a note in this melody that is *not* in the key of C major.

  (iv) How many times does the rhythm ♫ ♩ occur? ………

  (v) Give the letter name of the *lowest* note in the melody. ………

(c) Copy out the music from the start of bar 5 to the end of bar 8, exactly as it is written [10]
   above. Don't forget the clef and all other details. Write the music on the blank stave
   above question (a). (Marks will be given for neatness and accuracy.)

Theory Paper Grade 1 2016 S

Duration 1½ hours

TOTAL MARKS
100

Candidates should answer ALL questions.
Write your answers on this paper – no others will be accepted.
Answers must be written clearly and neatly – otherwise marks may be lost.

1   Add the missing bar-lines to these two melodies. The first bar-line is given in each.

10

2   Write a two-bar rhythm as an answer to the given rhythm.

10

3 (a) Give the letter name of each of the notes marked ∗, including the flat sign where necessary. The first answer is given.

Czerny

C
....

(b) How many bars contain a semiquaver (16th note)? ....

4 *Above* each note write a *higher* note to form the named *harmonic* interval, as shown in the first answer. The key is G major.

8th/8ve

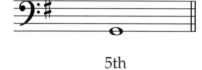

5th

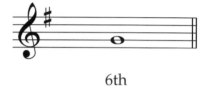

6th

7th

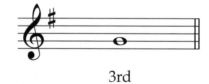

3rd

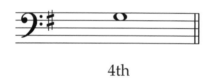

4th

5 (a) Draw a circle around the *higher* note of each of these pairs of notes.

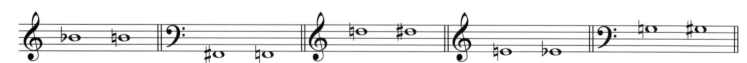

(b) Draw a circle around the *lower* note of each of these pairs of notes.

14

Music Theory
Past Papers
2016
Model Answers

ABRSM Grade 1

Welcome to ABRSM's *Music Theory Past Papers 2016 Model Answers*, Grade 1. These answers are a useful resource for students and teachers preparing for ABRSM theory exams and should be used alongside the relevant published theory past papers.

All the answers in this booklet would receive full marks but not all possible answers have been included for practicable reasons. In these cases other reasonable alternatives may also be awarded full marks. For composition-style questions (where candidates must complete a rhythm, compose a melody based on a given opening or set text to music) only one example of the many possible answers is given.

For more information on how theory papers are marked and some general advice on taking theory exams, please refer to the Music Theory Grade 1 web page: www.abrsm.org/theory1.

Using these answers

- Answers are given in the same order and, where possible, in the same layout as in the exam papers, making it easy to match answer to question.

- Where it is necessary to show the answer on a stave, the original stave is printed in grey with the answer shown in black, for example:

- Alternative answers are separated by an oblique stroke (/) or by *or*, for example:

    getting slower / gradually getting slower

- The old-style crotchet rest ![old rest] is accepted as a valid alternative to the modern symbol ![modern rest] .

- Answers that require the candidate to write out a scale or chord have been shown at one octave only. Reasonable alternatives at different octaves can also receive full marks.

- Sometimes the clef, key and time signature of the relevant bar(s) are included for added clarity, for example:

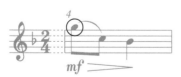

Theory Paper Grade 1   2016   A
Model Answers

1 (10)

(a)

(b)

2 *There are many ways of completing this question. The specimen completion below would receive full marks.* (10)

3 (10)

4 (10)

(a) 5th 2nd 1st / 6th 8th / 4th 7th 5th 3rd
             8th / 8ve   8ve / 1st

(b)

3

5  (10)

6 (10)

5 ♪ ♩ ♩ 𝅗𝅥 𝅗𝅥. 𝅝 (10)

6 (10)

7 (10)

(a)

(b) D F♯ A   G B D

8 (a) at a walking pace / medium speed (10)
100 crotchets in a minute / 100 quarter notes in a minute/
      100 crotchet beats in a minute / 100 quarter-note beats in a minute
very quiet / very soft
accent / forced / accented
getting louder / gradually getting louder

(b) (10)

    (i)   semibreve / whole note
    (ii)   6; 7
    (iii)   *legato* (smoothly)
    (iv)   3 / 7
    (v)   E

(c) (10)

Theory Paper Grade 1   2016   B
Model Answers

1   (10)

(a)

2 *There are many ways of completing this question. The specimen completion below would receive full marks.*   (10)

3   (10)

4   (10)

(a)   G E D B G F♯ C A F♯

(b)   *There are two possible answers to this question. Either of the answers shown would receive full marks.*

5

6 (10)

7 (10)

8 (a)   fast / quick / cheerful / lively (10)
                crotchet beats / quarter-note beats
                loud
                very quiet / very soft
                play the notes smoothly / slur

   (b) (10)

        (i)   dotted minim / dotted half note
        (ii)   C / middle C
        (iii)   two
        (iv)   *There are three possible answers to this question. Any of the brackets shown would receive full marks.*

        (v)   6th

(c)   (10)

Theory Paper Grade 1   2016   C
Model Answers

1   (10)

2 *There are many ways of completing this question. The specimen completion below would receive full marks.*   (10)

3   (10)

4   (10)

5   (10)

6 6th   3rd   4th   (10)
       8th / 8ve   7th   5th

7   (10)

(a)   5th   4th   2nd   8th /   7th   6th   5th   3rd   1st /
                                 8ve / 1st   8th / 8ve

(b)   four

8 (a)   fast / quick / cheerful / lively   (10)
             the number of beats in a bar / two beats in a bar
             very loud
             play the notes detached / jumpy / staccato
             play the notes smoothly / slur

      (b)   (10)
             (i)   quaver / eighth note
             (ii)   5
             (iii)

             (iv)   three
             (v)   G

      (c)   (10)

8

Theory Paper Grade 1   2016   S
Model Answers

1 (10)

2 *There are many ways of completing this question. The specimen completion below would receive full marks.* (10)

3 (10)

(a)   C   E   B♭   A   D   F   C   G   F

(b)   two

4 (10)

5 (10)

(a)

(b)

Key   D major

Key   G major

Key   F major

7   G major   C major   D major   (10)
     C major   F major   D major

8   (a)   moderate speed / moderately   (10)
            moderately loud / half loud / medium loud
            getting louder / gradually getting louder
            accent / forced / accented
            getting slower / gradually getting slower

   (b)   (10)

       (i)   *There are five possible answers to this question. Any of the brackets shown would receive full marks.*

       (ii)   C / middle C
       (iii)   *staccato* (detached)
       (iv)   two
       (v)   8 / last bar

   (c)   (10)

4

*Throughout the volume, the two notes in this part offer alternatives:
sing the upper, lower or both as you wish.

Consider yourself/Who will buy?
(Oliver)

Text & music: Lionel Bart

Memory
(Cats)

Music: Andrew Lloyd Webber
Text: Trevor Nunn after T.S. Eliot